A PONY
for a
Day

June Crebbin

OXFORD
UNIVERSITY PRESS

OXFORD
UNIVERSITY PRESS

Great Clarendon Street, Oxford, OX2 6DP, United Kingdom

Oxford University Press is a department of the University
of Oxford. It furthers the University's objective of excellence
in research, scholarship, and education by publishing
worldwide. Oxford is a registered trade mark of Oxford
University Press in the UK and in certain other countries

Text © June Crebbin 2014

The moral rights of the author have been asserted

First published 2014

All rights reserved. No part of this publication may
be reproduced, stored in a retrieval system, or transmitted,
in any form or by any means, without the prior permission in
writing of Oxford University Press, or as expressly permitted
by law, by licence or under terms agreed with the appropriate
reprographics rights organization. Enquiries concerning
reproduction outside the scope of the above should be sent to the
Rights Department, Oxford University Press, at the address above.

You must not circulate this work in any other form
and you must impose this same condition on any acquirer

British Library Cataloguing in Publication Data
Data available

ISBN: 978-0-19-830798-3

10 9 8 7 6 5

Paper used in the production of this book is a natural,
recyclable product made from wood grown in sustainable forests.
The manufacturing process conforms to the environmental
regulations of the country of origin.

Printed in China by Golden Cup

Acknowledgements

Series Editor: Nikki Gamble

Illustrations by Julia Patton
Photography by Bob Langrish
Additional imagery by OUP

Thanks to Summerhouse Equestrian Centre
and to our models Zara and Martine

Contents

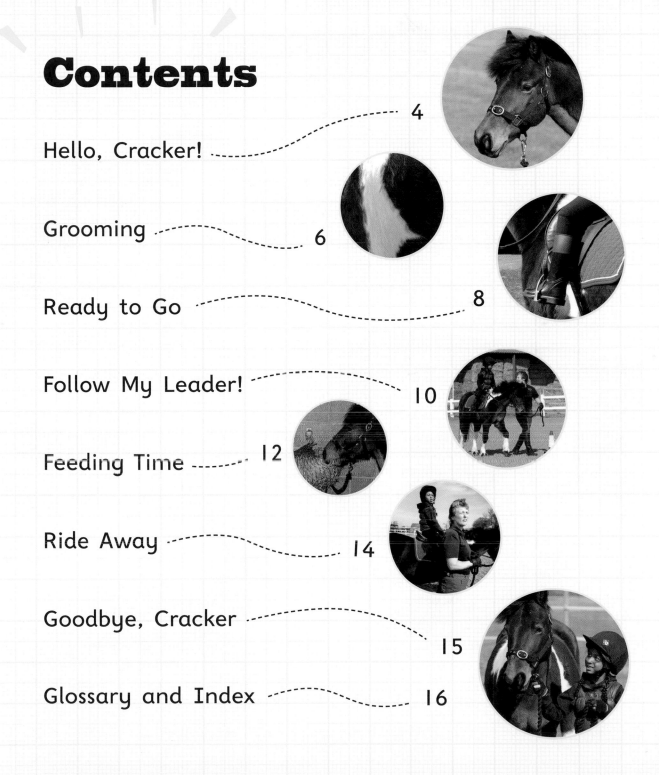

Hello, Cracker!

Ella was at a riding school. She was very excited. She was going to ride a pony and look after it all day!

But which one?

Meg

Ella

Hello, Cracker!

Meg showed her Cracker. His coat was brown and white. He had a black **mane**.

mane

148 cm

Cracker

tail

A pony can be up to 148 cm high, from the ground to the top of its back.

Hello, Ella! I'm a bit muddy!

5

Grooming

Cracker needed to be **groomed**. Ella brushed the mud off Cracker's coat. It was hard work!

Meg showed her how to scrape the mud out of Cracker's foot. That was hard work, too, but Ella wanted to have a go.

Up, Cracker, Up!

dandy brush:
to rub off mud

hoof-pick:
to clean feet

wall: the
hard outside
covering of
the hoof

sole

frog: the soft
part of the foot

Mind my frog!

Ready to Go

Ella couldn't wait to ride Cracker. She helped to put on his **bridle** and **saddle**.

She did up the **girth** under his tummy. Cracker was ready to ride!

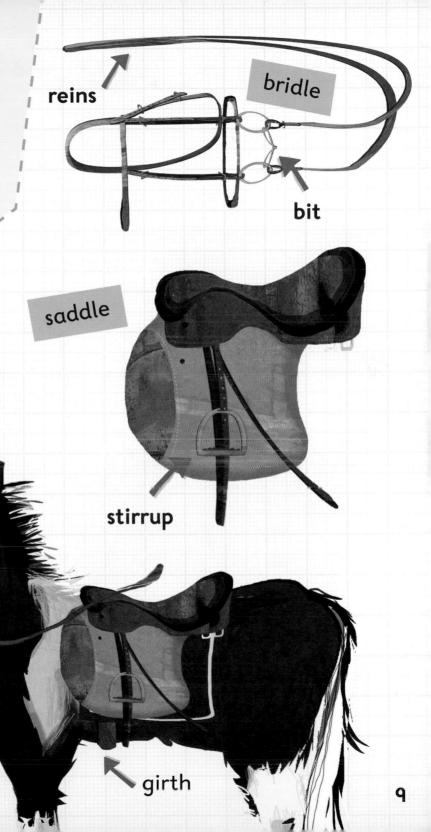

reins

bridle

bit

saddle

stirrup

girth

Let's go!

Follow My Leader!

Ella put on a hard hat. She was ready to ride!

In the **arena**, Meg helped Ella to **mount**. She felt really high up! Other children were there riding ponies, too.

First they walked round in a circle. Then they steered round some cones.

Cracker knocked one over!

When you ride, you must wear a hard hat.  This can usually be borrowed at the riding school.

You might also wear:

jodhpurs
(*say* jod-perz)

gloves

T-shirt

Oops! Better steering next time, please!

jumper

jacket

Feeding Time

By the end of the morning, Ella felt very hungry. Before she had lunch, she helped to fill a hay-net for Cracker. He was hungry, too.

There you are, Cracker!

Ponies mostly eat fresh grass or hay (dried grass).

Ponies always need water in their stable or out in the field.

Munch, munch. Yum!

Ride Away

After lunch, everyone set off down the lane. They rode along a track and over a stream. Ella and Cracker liked splashing through the water!

On the way back, a car driver wanted to get past. Meg steered Cracker to the side of the lane.

Good steering!

If drivers are careful when they pass you, always smile and nod to say thank you.

14

Goodbye, Cracker

When they arrived back at the riding school,
Ella helped to take off Cracker's bridle and saddle.

She gave Cracker a big hug
and a carrot.

What a day! It was
the best day of her life.

When you give your
pony a carrot, always
hold your hand flat.

Thank you,
Cracker!

Goodbye, Ella.
Come back soon!

Glossary

arena: an area for riding

bit: the part of the bridle that goes in the pony's mouth

bridle: the equipment that fits on the pony's head

girth: a strap to hold the saddle in place

groomed: cleaned and brushed

jodhpurs: trousers for riding which are tight from the knee to the ankle

mane: the long hair on the pony's neck

mount: get onto the pony's back

reins: straps held by the rider to steer the pony

saddle: a seat on the back of the pony

stirrup: a metal loop to hold the rider's foot

Index